# Adventures in
# *Embodiment*

# Adventures in
# *Embodiment*

Using somatic awareness as a tool for growth,
health, recovery, and self-discovery

by LindaChristy Weiler. M.S.

Illustrated by Jennifer Weiler

Belle Rive Press
Nashville, TN
2009

First Printing 2009

Printed in the United States of America

ISBN 0–9701402–8-2

To my friend Frankie.

Acknowledgments

A heartfelt thank-you to my husband David R. Weiler for his computer knowledge, technical support, assistance with photographic details, and generous endorsement of this project. Most of all, I am thankful for his encouragement and inspiration.

I would also like to acknowledge the bountiful efforts of my daughter Jennifer, who is seventeen and a senior in high school as we are completing this project. Thank-you for creating such beautiful and inspirational art, and for graciously allowing me to showcase it in this text. Jennifer is also the author of *Crystal's Reflection* and *Rosalyn and Delilah*, the two short stories in Chapter 3.

# contents

# chapter 1
## somatics          14

# chapter 2
## yoga          68

# preface

As long as you are living life as an embodied human, the life of your body is your life. Your body is your personal representative in the earthly realm of existence. In this text, we advocate the value of exploring embodiment as a valid means of getting to know your self.

If you are in need of replenishment, recovery, or searching for direction, meaning, or a dose of inspiration, this book is for you. We are especially interested in reaching out to anyone who has experienced a traumatic episode which required a psychological or somatic compensation strategy to manage survival and coping. We hope that the gentle, supportive, and aesthetically-pleasing nature of this text becomes an inspirational, informative, and enjoyable self-help resource.

Our goal is to help you develop an honest, insightful, and somatically-based understanding of your body and your self. We present a variety of purposeful opportunities to support self-awakening and self-healing, which include the following: yoga (a fundamental somatic awareness technique), creative writing (realizing and appreciating the collective consciousness), archetypes (exploring universal symbolism), and visual art (intuitive awakening though aesthetics). Essentially, each of these pathways teaches us that our perceptions, interpretations, and reactions originate from within our bodies. Though these internal sensations are not always tangible or observable, the subjective nature of somatic awareness is becoming recognized as a valid scientific method and an effective, viable modality for therapy and recovery.

Your first adventure in embodiment is an exploration into the wholistic practice of hatha yoga, which is presented as a gentle, therapeutic form of mind-body fitness. As you practice the postures, your primary focus should center on the introspective, self-sensing nature of the experience. This means that you will be learning about your self by learning to access, identify, and understand the messages, in the form of sensations, that arise from within your body.

Approached in an individualized way, yoga becomes a creative vehicle for self-discovery and self-improvement.

Your next adventure involves a very different path toward somatic awakening. Through reflections on symbolism, poetry and short stories, you will discover the commonality, familiarity, and sense of community that permeates our shared collective consciousness.

For your final adventure, you will delve into the sublime experience of appreciating and embracing the glory of the feminine consciousness. Throughout the text, and showcased in the final section, behold the expression of beauty and symbolism in Jennifer's inspirational Manga (Japanese-style) artwork. We hope that you will feel a powerful connection to the many aspects and mystique of the sacred feminine. As your exploration of embodiment evolves, we hope that you will learn to love, honor, and trust your authentic self.

Won't you join us on a somatic journey of emancipation?

- Explore the relationship between the body, mind, and spirit as experienced through embodiment and expressed though creativity.

- Treat your body as an ally for growth and understanding. Learn to access and process somatically-based material with the intent of modifying or refining your unconscious conditioning.

- Promote transpersonal growth through the conscious evolution and maturation of your authentic self. This process is undeniably related to and driven by evolved embodiment.

- Recognize the value of consciously relating to the feminine aspect of the universal spirit.

# introduction

Life as a human is a journey that begins with embodiment. The soma (living body) is a thriving manifestation that displays the bodily characteristics of your personality, your immediate condition, and your history. The soma is your most personal and tangible asset. If you feel comfort, acceptance, trust, and love for your own body, then you will feel comfort, acceptance, trust, and love for your own self. Likewise, if you have established a sense of stability, confidence and maturity in the relationship that exists between your body, your mind, and your spirit, you will tend to gravitate toward stable, confident, and mature relationships with others. Awareness of and respect for your body provides the essential groundwork for a happy, healthy, and meaningful existence. The cultivation, nourishment, and maintenance of a sincere, affirmative, and trusting affiliation with embodiment will keep you grounded in reality.

# somatics

*and the case for evolved embodiment*

# 1

Nowadays we are born into a cultural situation in which values have become warped and the importance of acting with integrity has been brushed aside. We grow up believing that what's most important about the body is how it looks, and what's most important about the mind is how much it earns. We live in a culture based on consumerism, and from an early age we are taught that more is better and we should always shoot for perfection. Our revered female role models are not just beautiful, they are perfectly beautiful. Too many of them are inappropriately skinny, shockingly promiscuous, self-absorbed and sassy. And too often they teach us that the self-destructive and bizarre behaviors associated with a toxic lifestyle can be fun, thrilling, and even acceptable.

Given these circumstances, it's pretty easy to see why we so many of us grow up feeling anxious, unaccepted, betrayed and unfulfilled. When nothing less than perfection is recognized as the goal, the bar has been set too high, and we cannot possibly compete. Though we try and try, we will never be the best at everything. We cannot always be the golden girl, the winner, the one who comes out on top.

We are chasing after a standard and a way of life that is both unreasonable and unattainable. It is a lifestyle that often goes against our better judgment, inherent value system, and sense of humanity. Time after time we end up feeling depressed, dejected, inadequate and lacking.

But maybe, just maybe, we will begin to see that it is the egotistical, self-absorbed existence itself which is flawed, and that we, as individuals, are just fine. This awareness indicates the beginning of a return to reality, and it typically includes a re-examination of priorities and a commitment to wellness in body and mind.

Congratulations! If you are lucky enough to recognize the error of your perfection-seeking ways, you have taken the first step toward recovery. The next step is acknowledging the dissolution of your mind-body connection and initiating the process of reconnection. Though your mind has been mistakenly pursuing the notion of a fairy tale existence, your body has been living in the real world. Your body knows that you are not a Goddess, a Princess, or a Heroine. Your body knows that you are fully capable of displaying plebian behaviors like temper tantrums, and experiencing ordinary sensations like hunger, fatigue, aches and pains. Though you might have fleeting moments of divinity or majesty, your quality of life won't improve until your mind reunites with your body and you recognize yourself as a simple human being living an embodied life. If you want to enjoy life, you must live it as your authentic self, and you must accept the fact that you are more ordinary than you are special.

Even as we grow into seemingly well-adjusted adults, at one time or another in our lives most of us have felt somewhat beaten down, overwhelmed, anxious, or tormented by the responsibilities and pace of daily life. Perhaps you survived a traumatic event but were never able to totally shed the victim consciousness. As a result you tend to withdraw or dissociate because you are very shy, insecure, or feel awkward in social situations. Or perhaps you have chosen to play the Drama Queen by acting out, running away from confrontation, and deriding authority figures.

All of these kinds of behaviors and reactions indicate the presence of a compensation strategy, which is a way of coping, surviving, and dealing with a traumatic experience. Compensation strategies are designed to help you maintain control.

On the level of embodiment, they are containment strategies. Containment manifests as physical symptoms of compression, constriction, tension, tightness, pain, fatigue or exhaustion. The mental symptoms associated with containment are anxiety, susceptibility, irrational fears, or suppressed rage.

On one hand, a compensation strategy is useful because it allows you to continue on with your life. On the other hand, every type of compensation strategy has negative side effects which will continue to compound until the compensatory behavior itself becomes an unforgiving issue that will need to be openly addressed.

**The most common types of compensation strategies are addictions and eating disorders.**

Can you see how compensation strategies are a form of self-imposed imprisonment? Why would we do this? Why would we restrict our own freedom as a means of survival? What makes so many of us adopt and rely on compensation strategies?

*manipulating embodiment*

# addictions

An addiction is a compensation strategy. It is a control strategy. It is an attempt to function in a world that does not seem safe. Addictive behaviors are attempts to achieve the universal goal that is shared by all those who suffer from a traumatic wound. That goal is denying reality.

An addict is terrified of reality and of her own body. In the formative years of childhood, somehow the addict learned that reality was not safe. Something happened in her young life to make her believe that her body was not safe from harm. Now, in present time, the addiction serves as a palliative device that helps to conceal or avoid her memories of loss, abuse, or abandonment. To alleviate anxiety and discomfort, she becomes dependent on the addiction to provide a temporary fix or a brief escape from the conscious or unconscious horrors associated with reality. The addict is desperately trying to extinguish stressful, frenzied feelings and the pent-up survival energy that permeates her body and self. The addiction is a compensation strategy that helps her avoid knowing and dealing with the truth.

On the surface the addict might appear to be quite ordinary, well adjusted, well liked, happy, and successful. But inside her body, she feels cramped and confined, agitated and unruly. To dull the somatic symptoms, she relies on the addiction to create an adrenaline rush of excitement (a 'high') or a peaceful interlude (a 'low'). This is a way of self-medicating, for the addictive substance typically provides a brief period in which both her body and her self feel better. For a little while, the reality of pain, anxiety, tension, fear, a hectic pace, and a multitude of responsibilities are temporarily suspended in favor of a freer and easier fantasy existence. For a little while, she can be carefree and content.

Yet for the addict, the pursuit of contentment will never end until she grounds herself in reality by re-connecting with her body. Embracing embodiment will support the healing processes of introspection, re-education, and recovery.

*rejecting embodiment*

# eating disorders

Eating disorders are another type of compensation strategy based on issues of control. Self-denial of food, self-denial of the body, and self-denial of feelings are the hallmarks of eating disorders.

In the realm of eating disorders, the anorexic, in particular, has lost touch with embodied reality. To a certain extent, the anorexic is no longer living in the real world, for if she were, she would see her body as it truly is – emaciated. And she would feel her body as it really is – suffering and starving for nourishment. Yet she dismisses the fact that her body has become weak, malnourished, and can no longer maintain its beauty and vitality. Because she is living a fantasy existence in which a lesser or diminished amount of bodily substance is mistakenly associated with safety and divinity, she simply doesn't see or sense that her body is withering away. Sadly, this perverted viewpoint based on self-denial and mistreatment is the only source of control that she thinks she has.

"I don't trust what I see in the mirror. I don't trust myself. The only way to stay in control is to become less and less noticeable. When I dissolve into nothingness, then, and only then, will I be safe."

In terms of somatic-psychology, an anorexic suffers from a lack of solid substance (adequate and appropriate body weight) which produces a lack of grounding. Perhaps unconsciously, the anorexic is removing herself from the human realm by reducing the weight and mass of her body. In effect, she is denying and destroying her own embodiment.

The anorexic believes that extreme thinness is ethereal, and that by being thinner than the rest of us, she is better than the rest of us.

Oddly enough, as her body occupies less space the anorexic experiences a kind of euphoria associated with lightness of being. She is proud of her disciplined self-denial and wears her unnaturally thin body as a badge of honor. Secretly she delights in the glory of becoming a celestial being. She longs to be light, expansive, uncontained, unbound, and free from matters of the flesh. But she is confusing the intangible and unbound sensation of emptiness and nothingness with spirituality and worth.

"I am a good girl. I am heavenly. I am pure and unbound." But the hidden message speaks the truth. "I cannot be touched or manipulated. I am becoming invisible. And then I will be safe."

The anorexic simultaneously succeeds at dulling her appetite for food and for life. She accomplishes this by denying her body what it needs to sustain health and life. As she severely restricts the passage of food through her digestive tract, the spaciousness, volume, and tone in the guts is reduced. If there is very little or nothing going through the digestive system, then there is very little or nothing that needs to be processed, assimilated, and eliminated. Without adequate digestive activity (in terms of movement and substance), the abdominal region will shrink and contract. Prolonged abdominal contraction will eventually produce intra-abdominal confinement which stifles bodily sensations and bottles-up emotions, making them less accessible.

"I am empty. I am a void. No one can control me and no one can harm me because I feel nothing. I am invincible."

Restricting adequate space and substance in the guts is a containment strategy based on the psychological need to gain control. This is nothing less than a psycho-somatic survival strategy, for along with dulling the body's message of hunger she has also dulled the messages that indicate emotional pain such as grief, shame, guilt, anxiety, confusion, or fear. If she continues to dismiss the body's hunger signals long enough, eventually the entire somatic message system will shut down and all of the body's appetites will be suspended. There is a flaw in this strategy, but the anorexic does not see it. The problem is that her body cannot successfully curtail negative emotions while allowing positive emotions. For the body, differentiation is not possible. It's all or none. The elimination of pleasurable sensations is a trade off for achieving the elimination of emotional pain.

To be healed, the anorexic must relearn how to find pleasure in eating and not feel guilty about it. She must slowly rebuild and balance the relationship between her body (matter) and her spirit (spaciousness, lightness). As she learns to accept, honor, and trust her embodiment, she will learn to accept, honor, and trust her self. But there is also a crucial somatically-based problem that must be addressed and overcome. The problem is that the anorexic experiences the sensations of inner weight, fullness, and satiety (from eating a meal) as uncomfortable and even painful. As peristalsis is reactivated, her shrunken intestines and inactive stomach will ache as the digestive tract stretches and slowly returns to life. The unfamiliar feeling of internal fullness might make her feel sluggish, gross, gluttonous, awkward, stuffed and stifled, for she has grown familiar with and comforted by the sensations of hunger, emptiness, and weightlessness, which to her indicate self-discipline and control. Though most of us immediately recognize hunger and inner emptiness as sensations of suffering, the anorexic mistakenly identifies them as sensations of ascendency. To us this is a perplexing response, but for the anorexic it has become a learned truth.

Ballet dancers, due to their need to appear thin, lithe and weightless, are another population that could benefit from grounding and self-nurturing. Ballet dancers are masters of discipline and self-denial. They are dedicated and driven, achievement-oriented, appearance-oriented, and fervently deny hunger, ignore pain, and reject anything that does not involve the dance world. Weight control often becomes a singular focus in their lives, to the extent that everything they do is to maintain the desirable physique. Athletes can be equally dedicated and driven. They can also suffer from a distorted body image, bizarre eating rituals, self denial, and the drive for perfection. Likewise, genetically thin and small-framed individuals are often in need of proper grounding, and must make an effort to maintain an appropriate balance between the sensations of substance (weight of the body) and ether (lightness of spirit). All of these types of people must take care to avoid becoming infatuated with the pursuit of lightness and thinness. This is sometimes surprisingly difficult for them, because the desire to achieve a waiflike body image can become very seductive and euphoric.

In moderation, disciplined behaviors of self-denial can be effective training strategies. But when these behaviors occur in excess, they become counterproductive. They become addictions. To recover from eating disorders, an individual must embrace embodiment and establish a firmer, more grounded sense of self. Re-learning to appreciate the feeling of fullness is important because it provides a reality check that calls our attention to embodiment, to abundance, and to the actual experience of the present moment.

Life as a human
is tied to the life
of the body,
so to deny or denigrate
one's embodiment
is to deny life itself.

*Journal Entry:*

My mother was 18 and unmarried when I was born. My father left us when I was three months old. A few years later my mother got married to another man and had four more children. I never felt like I was part of that family. I never felt like I fit in. I was overweight and a disgrace to my mom. So for a while I lived with my grandparents.

When I started high school it was decided that I should live with my father and his new wife. One day I came home from school to find an empty house. All of the furniture was gone and my father and my step mother were gone. They had secretly moved away while I was at school that day. No one told me. All that was left in the house was the telephone. I called a girl friend and her mom came to get me. I lived with that family for the last two years of high school. I never heard from my father again.

I was fat for most of my life, but luckily I had the 'happy gene.' I could put on a happy face and act like everything was fine. I guess that was something I learned while growing up. If you were happy and funny then everyone would like you, even if you were fat. When I turned 40 I decided that I would never be fat again. I lost 60 lbs and never looked back. Now I am 74 years old. I am very blonde, very thin, very cheerful and very funny. Everyone seems to like me.

*Sometimes I still wonder
how I managed to survive
my childhood.
Sometimes I still wonder
who I really am.
And sometimes
I wonder
if I like myself.
I think that maybe I do.*

# sorting and re-arranging
*seeking order*

An individual who displays the sorting, re-arranging, and improvement-seeking syndrome is chasing perfection and control by desperately seeking order. Some of these people spend Friday nights re-arranging the living room furniture. Others are compulsive about cleanliness and keep every little thing in its proper place. For many women and girls, this compensation strategy manifests in the form of continual body improvement. She will seek out the newest self-help book, the latest fashion, another type of massage therapy, better shoes, better vitamins, better make-up, or a better hairstyle. She spends a large percentage of her time, money, and thoughts working on self-improvement. In an ongoing attempt to get it right, she keeps reliving the same behavioral pattern over and over. She keeps telling herself that "maybe this will be the fix I need."

If this sounds like you, did you ever stop to wonder why you feel the need to keep improving or fixing your body and your self? Do you think that this is normal behavior? Have you actually convinced yourself that it is *honorable* behavior, because your goal is self-improvement? Can you see that these behaviors are characteristic of someone who is seeking acceptance? Have you ever thought that maybe, just maybe, this pattern of behavior is a type of addiction?

Sorting and rearranging behaviors can even show up during activities that are based on healthy habits or good intentions, like practicing yoga. When learning a yoga posture, these behaviors will display as fidgiting, periodic readjusting and shifting, and an inability to get comfortable, stay focused, and remain still. The repeated question "Am I doing it right?" indicates a desperate need for perfection and appearance orientation.

Likewise, anyone who proclaims that she could never go a single day without exercising should examine her true motive, for sometimes what appears to be dedication is really an addiction in disguise.

# the manufactured self
*"I am not enough"*

Some of the most common contemporary compensation strategies have actually become socially acceptable, and in some cases, commended by society. For example, being a hard worker, sacrificing yourself for others, and being thin are all considered legitimate and praiseworthy attributes. Yet even these stereotypical 'good girl' behaviors, when carried to excess or driven by a compensatory attitude, indicate the presence of an addiction.

We all know someone who devotes or gives of herself in a habitual or compulsive way. She is always upbeat and energetic, and eagerly attends to whatever is expected of her. To this end, she meticulously manufactures a super-sized Self who appears to be a perfect wife, a capable mother, a sexy siren and a popular participant with the in-crowd. She might be your mother, your neighbor or your friend. She might be you.

Yet unbeknownst to others, and possibly even unbeknownst to her own true Self, she is driven by a compensatory attitude. She might think that "if I am thin enough, then I will be attractive and popular," and her compulsive behavior will display as an eating disorder. Or "if I work hard enough, everyone will see how competent and capable I am." Her compensation strategies are quite ingenious, because any type of fatigue, pain, or suffering that is the direct result of being busy, working hard, or laboring to keep your body attractive is considered socially acceptable and admirable. Furthermore, these compensation strategies are also effective distraction or avoidance devices that keep her too busy or too tired to deal with other issues such as marital or money problems.

Though the underlying problem of low self esteem (and the need for approval) emerges from the realm of the psyche, her sense of satisfaction, which is based on her artificially manufactured super-sized Self, arises from an embodied reference point.

"My body is tired." This means that I am 'good enough' because I have worked hard.

"My body is exhausted." This means that I am 'good enough' because I exercised for six hours.

"My body is always busy." This means that I am 'good enough' because I have worked hard to take care of my family's needs.

"My body is hungry." This means that I am 'good enough' because I am thin.

In moderation, these types of behaviors are not necessarily counterproductive, but they must be balanced and tempered in a way to ensure a healthy and fulfilling existence. At one time or another, most of us need to step back for a reality check. Sometimes we need to examine our own motives by asking tough questions and giving honest answers.    What am I willing to sacrifice to maintain the appearance of competency, fortitude, and success? Why do I feel competitive or depressed when I meet someone younger, smarter, thinner, prettier, or richer than I am? Is feeling stressed-out, drained or overwhelmed a healthy and balanced state of being? Is skipping meals and checking my weight five times per day on the bathroom scale a dignified type of existence? Are these the types of behaviors that I want to model for my children? At the end of my life, do I really want to look back and grieve for the years that I carelessly gave away because I was trying to fulfill someone else's idea of excellence?

Did I ever live as my authentic self?

*a cry for help*

# desperate moments

Most people try to avoid pain. That is why those of us who are living in a state of depression, discontent, or anxiety often turn to an addictive substance. We use the addiction as a crutch or a coping mechanism that brings temporary relief. For a brief time we are able to enjoy a few moments of seemingly trouble-free and worry-free existence. For a brief time we have brought light to the darkside of the soul. For a brief time, we have dulled the pain.

*Journal Entry:      It seems like I've always suffered from joint pain, muscle pain, and chronic stomach aches. The only time that my body didn't hurt was when I was exercising. That's because exercise always made me feel alive and less stressed. Even though I would be sweaty, stinky, hot, and tired, hard exercise made me feel good. Maybe it was the endorphins or maybe I liked feeling the strength and power of my working muscles. Maybe it was a sense of accomplishment. Afterward, I would be exhausted. But that was another perk. Now I felt like I deserved to rest, relax, and do nothing. I felt like I deserved to eat. And I was too tired to worry or care about my problems.*

But for some people, pain is what makes them feel alive. For them, the sensation of pain is a remedy for numbness and lack of feelings. Pain confirms their existence as an embodied human. In a similarly misguided way, seeing your own blood and feeling the searing sensation created by self-inflicted cutting can provide satisfying emblems of embodiment. Sometimes tatoos fulfill the same general purpose. They serve as a visual and somatic reminder of a painful, profound, difficult, or life-changing experience.

If you have ever been trapped, either physically or psychologically, in a very dark, dreary, cold and confined place, you have known the feeling of desperation. And you have undoubtedly learned that during moments of desperation it is almost impossible to remember that the bright light of a new day will come. You might tell yourself that "It doesn't matter" and "I don't care." But the truth is that you do care, and it does matter. In those darkest moments when it seems that there is absolutely no way to recover or resolve the problems and issues that haunt you, the way back to sanity is found by returning to your body's consciousness and doing something physical. Walk, run, ride a bike, hike, swim, shoot baskets, or practice yoga postures. Do something physical until the moment of desperation passes. Let your body help you to feel better.

*trauma and the*
# body of evidence

The term 'body of evidence' refers to the embodied imprinting that occurs in accordance with an individual's perceptions and reactions to the numerous joys and frustrations that she encounters throughout daily life. Negative manifestations of the 'body of evidence,' such as chronic muscular tension, shallow breathing, and a rigid jaw are typically associated with trauma. Though trauma is actually a psychological wound, it also manifests as latent bodily damage. Trauma of any type qualifies as a life-altering experience, and will produce a change or adjustment that is reflected in both the body and the mind.

*Traumatic stress leaves a somatic footprint in the body.*

In the process of growing up, each of us has experienced moments of frustration, defeat, rejection, embarrassment, loss, or betrayal. Whether the traumatic experience was a single occasion or a series of ongoing violations, and whether it involved a close family member or a total stranger, experiences of this type can produce a greater or lesser degree of psycho-social and psycho-somatic impairments.

Fortunately, the body is very resourceful when it comes to self-protection and survival techniques. In the face of danger, the body instantly responds by preparing for fight or flight. Unfortunately there are certain circumstances in which fight or flight options are not available, and you must, by default, choose immobilization. You freeze (as in 'frozen with fear'). In this case, stillness is your final option for escape. Stillness is used to simulate invisibility or death, or to represent surrender and compliance.

The problem is that immobility causes you to embody your burdens. From the victim's perspective, the traumatic event was never successfully resolved. In this case, the highly activated emotional and physical states were never fully discharged, and psychological recovery was never completed. The traumatic situation never reached an acceptable conclusion in which self control and fear-free living could continue. In an ongoing attempt to suppress or contain the perpetual arousal response, the body compensates through somatic confinement strategies such as a pinched belly, a clenched jaw, hunched shoulders, and a stifled breath. On some level (maybe on many different levels) of consciousness, the traumatized individual will continue to re-play the traumatic event over and over again in many different ways, constantly seeking resolution and acceptable completion in the form of a positive, life affirming outcome that effectively nullifies the victim consciousness.

Traumatic stress can produce habitual feelings of helplessness, hopelessness, hyper-arousal, chronic tension, anxiety, and anger turned inward. You might experience compensatory episodes of withdrawing, acting out (revolutionary acts or behaviors), or re-enacting. You might display inappropriate outbursts of anger, fear, mistrust, or self-loathing. It might seem like other people are happier, have deeper friendships, and are more competent and capable than you are. Your life might seem highly dramatic, unproductive, and lack direction. If not addressed and resolved, the impairments caused by traumatic stress can last a lifetime.

Even a relatively mild traumatic experience can result in a degree of absence regarding somatic, social and territorial knowledge. Developmentally, you are 'frozen in time,' for the growth and maturation of your emotional intelligence has been interrupted. On the surface you are functioning as a reasonably rational adult, but on a deep subconscious level you feel interminably fearful and vulnerable.

Amazing as it may seem, it is not uncommon for the mind to experience total amnesia for the traumatic event, leaving you with no concrete evidence (in the form of accessible memories) as to why you always feel anxious or alienated. When deemed necessary for survival, forgetting is a viable psychological coping mechanism.

If parts of your past are hazy or if you have poor recall regarding portions of your childhood, you might be experiencing amnesia for a traumatic event.

Mental amnesia is always accompanied by some kind of physical amnesia. Known as sensori-motor amnesia, this somatic deadening or numbing can occur locally within a particular area of a specific body part or it can be experienced as an overall dulling of bodily sensations.    Sensori-motor amnesia creates a lack of conscious connection (an inability to accurately sense) and lack of conscious control (an inability to manage efficiently and effectively), and is associated with a curtailment in the ability to experience and express emotions honestly and appropriately. Even though the conscious mind appears to have recovered from the traumatic episode by simulating sanity, the body carries the evidence in the form of somatic scars.

To be healed, talk therapy is often not enough. No amount of discussion or dialog will let you relive that traumatic moment and change the past. To be healed, you must attend to your present state. In many cases, maybe most cases, permanent resolution can only by accomplished by addressing the somatic arousal residue that has remained trapped in the body. To be healed, the body's stagnant reservoir of highly charged survival energy must be allowed to surface so that it can be dealt with (adequately explored and discharged), once and for all.

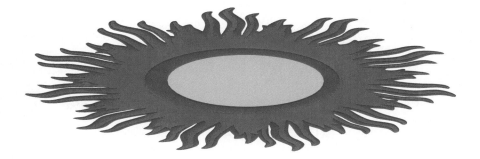

As part of the recovery process, you must understand and accept the fact that what was lost cannot totally be recaptured, and you must somehow weave the details of the traumatic event into the fabric of your consciousness. You do this by accessing, identifying, reporting, processing, and assimilating the effects that the event had on all aspects of your self – physical, mental, and spiritual. You do this by exploring embodiment. Even if many years have passed since the original traumatic event occurred, you can still learn how to manage, reduce, and possibly even eliminate the undesirable somatic and psychological aftereffects of historical trauma. You do this by freeing the body of specific holding patterns and reducing the body's tension level. As physical tension subsides and the autonomic system normalizes, anxiety will diminish. Gradually, both body and mind will shift toward better balance and stability.

Little by little, there is a re-germination of self care and self love. Healthy relationships and trust are carefully rebuilt. The capacity to live and appreciate the ordinary events of daily life is gradually restored, while the need to be considered special, to be rescued, or to remain isolated is no longer requisite. A more stable, secure, and comfortable perspective toward your body, toward your self, toward others, and toward life begins to emerge. These types of changes indicate growth and forward movement in the processes of recovery and healing.

From the broader perspective of restorative justice, you must eventually embrace the understanding that each individual is valuable and worthy, and that healing requires redemption at many levels and for all those involved. The victim heals through forgiveness. The perpetrator heals through apology and assumption of responsibility. And the community heals through fair and just restitution. To be fully effective, healing must provide rehabilitation for all participants, even bystanders. Each of us shares in the responsibility as caretakers and creators of a collective consciousness that is characterized by honor and integrity.

*Journal Entry:*

*When I was 37 years old, I began to have memories of childhood sexual abuse. Initially, there was a lot of denial, uncertainty, and questioning. But eventually, as I accepted the reality of the situation, the big picture of my lifetime began to fall into place. Now that I knew the truth, my whole life made sense. Now I understood why I had no clear recollections of my childhood and why I sometimes displayed bizarre behaviors, crazed reactions, and destructive repetitive patterns throughout my life. Now I understood why I never believed that I could count on anyone to be there for me in a crisis. Now I understood why I never wanted to feel like I owed a debt of gratitude to anyone. Now I knew why I never trusted anyone completely.*

*Accepting and coming to terms with the terrible truth of my childhood was not a fun or easy thing to do, but in a strange way it made me feel better. Despite the fact that I had spent most of my life acting as a quasi-psycho, somehow there was great comfort in knowing that I had a reason for acting that way.*

*With acceptance came a release from habitual physical tension. I started breathing better and my shoulders relaxed. I could finally sit and walk without tensing my buttocks. My normally clenched jaw was also beginning to release and relax.*

*Finally, I could live as a protagonist in my own life. But I had a lot of catching up to do. I had a lot of growing up to do, for it was as if my emotional development had been interrupted at the age when the abuse occurred. As a natural part of my healing journey, I needed to repair my underdeveloped social skills. Eagerly, I observed others. I studied and learned how normal people behaved and interacted. Then I consciously adjusted, improved, and practiced the proper and socially acceptable ways of speaking, moving, and behaving. Though I was 37 years old, in many ways I was just beginning to live as an adult.*

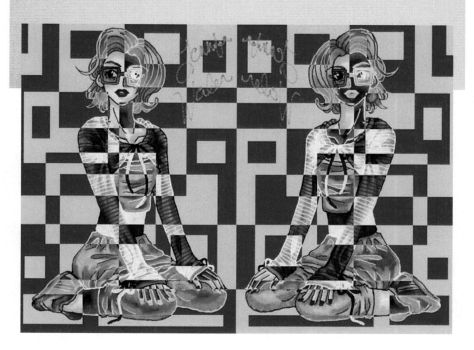

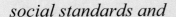

*social standards and*
# the false feminine

In addition to trauma, there is a second source of frustration that feeds a widespread inferiority complex among humans. It is an underhanded, malicious form of indoctrination which preys on our fear of inadequacies by assigning demeaning attributes to the feminine aspect of consciousness. It creates extreme tendencies toward either submission or domination, and it delights in the victim consciousness. It is known as the false feminine.

What are the messages that society is sending us regarding femininity? Are they positive or negative? Are they life affirming or inherently destructive? To be accepted and loved, must we always display a cheerful, courteous, and submissive demeanor? Must we always have a slender, sexy body? Must we always wear high-heeled shoes and make our hair a lighter, brighter shade of blonde? Must we always put the needs of others before our own? Perhaps we have, for too long, allowed ourselves to be indoctrinated by the media. Perhaps we have grown accustomed to artificiality and over-consumption. Perhaps we have traded away a portion of our souls by unknowingly aligning ourselves with the personification of the false feminine.

Historically, the false feminine upholds rigid requirements for what defines the proverbial 'good girl.' Yet at the same time, the false feminine proclaims that the 'naughty girl' is potentially even more attractive, desirable, and successful. The false feminine thinks that she is demonstrating her power and freedom by partaking in shocking, promiscuous, inappropriate, and self-absorbed behaviors. Yet deep inside, and often unbeknownst and denied even to her self, the false feminine is weak, fragile, and lacks substance. She has never developed life affirming character traits.

An individual who has succumbed to the false feminine is sustained by control strategies such as addictions, eating disorders, and other self-destructive behaviors. Such tactics might seem to serve her well for the short term, but in the long run they demand payback. Eventually, they will expose her lack of self-esteem and damage her body. And she has no backup plan, for she has achieved neither maturity nor independence and she cannot provide for herself. The cruel reality of the false feminine is revealed at last. She is simply a misguided and manufactured caricature. She is a plaything for others.

# psycho-social underpinnings
*of the false feminine*

There are two sociological factors that contribute to the compounding effect of the false feminine. They are (1) the demise of a secure sense of connection via relationships and community, and (2) an over-interest and over-value on the importance of the individual.

Without a secure sense of connection and community, you lack a reliable support system. You lack the camaraderie of affiliation, and have no need for conduct that supports mutual responsibility. Meanwhile, over-valuing the importance of the individual creates the egotistical 'me first, me best' mindset which cultivates a competitive urge that delights in personal superiority and personal power, even if this occurs at the expense and misfortune of others.

These two sociological factors have helped create a disturbing trend which includes the following:

## Pre-occupation with appearance

The false feminine displays an inordinate pre-occupation with appearance. She associates self worth with body image. She wants to appear appealing, perfectly coifed, and sexually available. Pre-occupation with appearance also includes adherence to other social standards or ideals such as choosing a prestigious college, wearing designer jeans, or doing whatever it takes to be part of the in-crowd.

## Self-absorption

This aspect of the false feminine is characterized by behaviors and thought patterns that indicate greed or self-absorption. She might be fixated on achieving fame, fortune, or some type of recognition that makes her feel special. Being ordinary or adequate is not enough and is not acceptable. She has a definite need to prove her self. She wants and needs to be better than the rest.

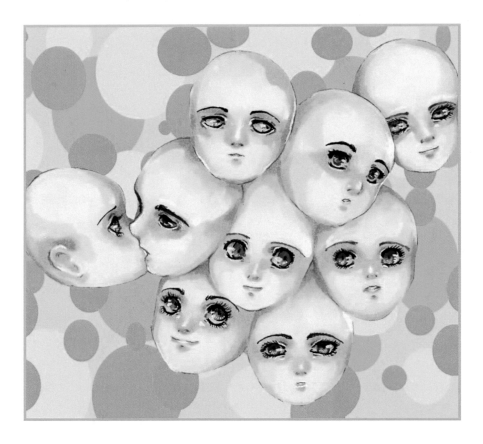

## Helplessness

The childlike, self-absorbed false feminine has never fully matured and is incapable of independence. She often finds herself trapped within boundaries created by a lack of know-how. These boundaries limit the possibilities that are available to her and keep her cornered, contained, and dependent. If left unchecked, dependency can produce helplessness, and helplessness can become hopelessness.

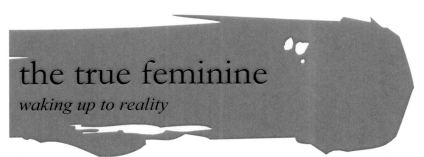

# the true feminine

*waking up to reality*

The accurate use of the term 'feminine' refers to qualities of integrity that are appropriate for both men and women, though these characteristics are generally attributed to a woman. When we speak of the feminine, we are referring to the concepts of nourishment, nurturing, balance, depth, peace, abundance, stillness, silence, compassion, truth-seeking, acceptance, forgiveness, contentment, being in tune with nature, self reflective, supportive, gentle, and persistent.

In the light of the true feminine, we see that the formation of the false feminine is nothing more than a misguided fairy tale about a female protagonist that has been placed on a pedestal or trapped in an ivory tower. As a result, she cannot escape and has never grown up. To survive, she has surrendered to the Evil Queen (false feminine). As long as she doesn't question authority, try to access memories of the past, or try to establish goals for the future, she will appear to be living reasonably well. She is functioning, but she is doing so in a hazy, semi-conscious state of confinement. Her only chance of salvation is being rescued by a Prince or father figure.

Far too many of us have bought into this surrealistic fantasy life. Far too many of us have been daydreaming our way through life. We tell ourselves that "If it's good enough, let it be." Don't ask questions. Don't rock the boat. Intuitively we know that we shouldn't look beneath the surface, for we might not like what we find. Intuitively, we know that the truth might be painful.

But every now and then, there is a valiant girl or woman who starts to wake up. She begins to realize that she is not satisfied with the way she has been living her life. She begins to realize that she has been living as an imaginary character, a caricature, and not as her true self. She wonders if there might be a better way.

*Journal Entry:*

*My body is my property. And I WANT MY BODY BACK. My ability to perceive, sense, and view the world has been skewed by past trauma in my life. My body remembers the trauma. My body protected me by locking, dissociating, or relying on destructive urges, crazy behaviors, and bizarre thought patterns. Repressed somatic trauma caused me to perceive the world as an unsafe and scary place. It caused me to perceive all people as untrustworthy and unreliable. I have been living in a habitual state of vigilance, and bracing against impending disaster. I have been living in a fantasy world based on fear. But now I am ready to wake up and return to life.*

Thankfully, there is a new era of the modern feminine on the horizon. This paradigm suggests that it is OK, even praiseworthy, to be a smart girl, to accept the natural structure, size, and shape of your body, to dress modestly and comfortably, to make your own decisions, and, when necessary, to disregard the social standards if you feel that they don't stack up. The new feminine is principled. She knows that knowledge is power. She paves and walks her own path, and she does so with integrity.

# mythology
*an inspirational resource for growth and transformation*

A myth is a story filled with metaphor and sacred symbolism that helps you to learn about yourself by witnessing the ritualistic transformation of an ordinary character into an archetype, heroine, or goddess. Stereotypically, the hero or heroine's task is to break free from oppression, manipulation, and culturally bound beliefs. She initiates this task by identifying and building her own resources. On a practical level, this is accomplished by contacting and connecting her soma and psyche.

Myths and inspirational fairy tales offer a sophisticated source of psychological resources that bypass intellectual ways of knowing. They awaken a longing, a remembrance, a sense of hope and faith in the possibility of living one's life in harmony and unity. They teach us that life's path is by no means straight or smooth, or particularly easy to find or to follow. They teach us that life's journey is about ups and downs, and that we are ever changing and ever evolving. They teach us that beauty is in the eye of the beholder, and that a life well lived requires more sincerity and more honesty than we are used to. It requires the discovery of our authentic self.

Though we can aspire toward the Goddess archetypes, we must not project idealized perfection onto ourselves and others. Time and time again we will be disappointed, frustrated, or ashamed when we or they do not live up to the grandeur of the imposed standard. We must remember that there is a difference between an archetypal image and human reality.

Light in the darkness
is a supreme metaphor
of the quest for
the authentic self

# amaterasu

*she who shines
in the
heavens*

Amaterasu is the mythological Japanese Shinto Sun Goddess. Her name means 'she who shines in the heavens.' Amaterasu represents an accurate, authentic, and inspirational role model of the true feminine. She is revered for the brightness, warmth, clarity and nourishment that her light provides. Her regalia is a sword, a jeweled necklace, and a mirror. Her attributes include integrity, harmony, balance, grace, order, and clarity. She is the only female chief goddess of a contemporary religion. According to Shintoism, there is no good and evil in the world; there is simply appropriateness and wrongness. Here is her story:

Disgusted with her brother because of his violence toward women (symbolized as destruction of her flower gardens), Amaterasu closed herself in a cave and refused to come out. Many other deities gathered outside her self-made isolation and tried to lure her out. Finally, upon hearing the laughter of the Gods as they watched the goddess Uzume perform a comical and obscene dance, Amaterasu

was overcome with curiosity and emerged. Seeing her self as radiant
light reflected in a mirror that had been set up outside the entrance to
the cave, she was amazed at her own brilliance - which she had never
seen before! She returned to the world, bringing with her the light
and renewal of life. Amaterasu was so bright and radiant that her
parents sent her up the Celestial Ladder to heaven, where she has
ruled ever since. She also created weaving and agriculture.

- The sword is a symbol of honor, indicating the high
  value placed on authentic and appropriate behavior.
  "The sword is my strength. The sword is my spine."

- The jeweled necklace is a symbol of beauty, order and
  cleanliness. "The jewels are my inner beauty. The
  jewels are my creativity and my sexuality."

- The mirror is symbolic of how our external lives
  (home, environment, and relationships) are reflections
  of our inner worlds (conscious and unconscious
  aspects of the mind). "The mirror reflects how I see
  the world around me. My view of the outer world is
  affected by the state of my inner world (self)."

Amaterasu's attributes reflect the stereotypical Japanese etiquette and cultural behaviors that promote mutual interdependence and maintain harmony. All of these attributes attempt to diminish or eliminate problems based on misunderstandings and falsity. These attributes act as antidotes to the false feminine by counteracting the demise of community and the over-valuing of the individual. Traditionally, the Japanese culture has high regard for a harmonious existence.

1. Integrity – to place high value on appropriate, honest and authentic behavior.
2. Harmony – to promote agreement and congruity in feelings, approach, action, and disposition.
3. Balance and Grace – to appreciate moderation and the role of aesthetics.
4. Order – to maintain and appreciate cleanliness and logical, methodical arrangements.
5. Clarity – to seek the truth in thought, word, and deed; to make an effort to understand and to be understood.

If you can get a brief glimpse of the attributes that are represented by Amaterasu's light, you will have begun the journey of recovery. Now your adventures in embodiment begin. Now you can move forward toward emancipation by seeking the true feminine, and by living as your authentic self.

*re-education through*
# evolved embodiment

Helplessness, self-absorption, and a pre-occupation with appearance are all characteristics of the false feminine, and they are all byproducts of incompetency. The obvious cure for incompetency is competency, which fuels self-confidence. You might not know it, but you have the potential to develop the skills and can-do attitude associated with competency right now. You have everything you need close at hand, because a can-do attitude is based in your body. Simple acts of physical competency provide fundamental lessons that promote self-esteem via somatic savvy. Acquiring an attitude of competency that is grounded in the reality of embodiment will initiate self-discovery and self-growth. Competency will help you shed the veil of the false feminine.

The sensations of embodiment, officially studied and known as the science of Somatics, are important because they register the bodily reactions that coexist with your mental perceptions, attitudes and understandings. This means that every thought causes a bodily reaction, though this reaction might be so mild and so subtle that you never notice it. It also means that every bodily reaction is an accurate and immediate reflection of what the mind perceives. Unfortunately, most people remain oblivious to the undeniable interrelationship between the body and the mind. Somewhere along the way, our bodies got lost in the shuffle.

Competency will help you shed
the veil of the false feminine.

Acknowledgment of the mind-body connection has been all but lost due to the business of our lives. We live life in the fast and noisy lanes. Our days are highly scheduled, hectic and hurried. We have too many choices available to us. We are barraged by too much stimuli and too many activities. We seem to be continually in pursuit, searching or seeking something, but our direction is unclear and our goal is uncertain. Yet in the realm of the collective unconscious, we all instinctively know that something very valuable has been lost.

Unlike indigenous people, we no longer value the innate wisdom of our bodies. We have lost touch with our land and our tribe. We take our bodies, our lives, and our blessings for granted. Few of us ever feel content and competent enough to settle down and give thanks for the simple pleasures of daily life. Most of us have lost a greater or lesser sense of self by overlooking the value and potential pleasure found in acknowledging and appreciating the glorious and remarkable gift of embodiment.

**The way back to competency and contentment is through evolved embodiment.**

*Evolved embodiment* refers to improved and more acute somatic awareness. It is a more conscious experience of embodiment. It represents a form of refinement through re-education based on enhanced awareness in which you gradually open up your body, open up your mind, and open up to the world around you. Metaphorically, you are 'waking up.' With this awakening comes release from containment and oppression, and your underlying attitude will miraculously shift from a state of shortage to abundance. Though you have not become any richer, prettier, or smarter, it will seem like your resources are now ample, even bountiful. You will begin to acknowledge all of the beauty, wonders, and possibilities that are available to you, for you will no longer be operating as a pawn or a pauper. As that stressful sense of urgency is subdued, you will feel more connected and content.

Evolved embodiment is about learning to access and interpret your personal somatic material. It is about recognizing how each experience affects you by asking the following types of questions: What does this particular experience (whether it is practicing a yoga posture, beholding artwork, reading a poem or book, attending a theatrical event, having dinner with a group of friends, solving a customer service problem) evoke within my body and mind? Do these bodily sensations indicate the activation of an emotion, instinct, or attitude? What psychological changes, in the form of responses, ideas, images, and memories have arisen in conjunction with these physical changes? How has my overall condition been affected?

Gradually you will learn how to assimilate or discharge the energies associated with your psycho-somatic responses in a timely way so that homeostasis and equanimity can be quickly and efficiently restored. With this ability, you take back control of your body and your life, and you will regularly make wise choices. As you learn to trust your authentic Self, you will thrive.

### Physical Benefits of Evolved Embodiment
- Reduction in aches, pains, and bodily tension
- Better posture, better breathing, increased energy
- Better relaxation, better digestion and elimination

General Benefits of Evolved Embodiment

o   Becoming more mindful

o   Becoming more receptive to new experiences

o   Letting go of the need to judge, criticize,
or continually seek perfection

   o   Coming to terms with the past

   o   Becoming less anxious and more
    confident

   o   Moving beyond comfort zones
    (overcoming limitations)

   o   Improving imagination and aesthetic
    appreciation

   o   Developing curiosity and interest

   o   Taking personal responsibility for
    your body, life, and self

*Journal Entry:*

*I used to hate being a human. I thought that so much of the human condition was despicable, insignificant, and self-serving. I convinced myself that I was different from the ordinary humans, that I was somehow special or magical. I thought that maybe I was an angel wearing a human body, and that I was a 'chosen one.' Yet at the same time, I always assumed that death was imminent. I was pretty sure that I would die at a young age.*

*Gradually, my perspective changed. I began to see that not all humans were hateful or evil. More and more, I noticed that there were good people doing good things. Sometimes I noticed people having fun and being nice to each other. Sometimes I had fun.*

*Once I saw a little girl hugging and loving her new puppy. Just for a moment, I remembered being that little girl. Just for a moment, I remembered being a happy little girl.*

*I started to see my life as a journey in the works. I started to believe that maybe my life would be long and full and complete.*

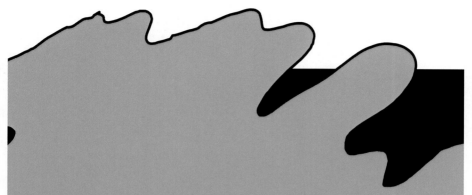

*Now I am a 24 years old, and I appreciate being 'ordinary.'*
*I enjoy knowing that I am part of a community of fellow humans.*
*Just like horses all share common horse bodies and horse*
*behaviors, and birds all share common bird bodies and bird*
*behaviors, we humans all share common human bodies and human*
*behaviors.*

*On the surface our personalities and appearances make us*
*seem unique and different. But underneath, where is counts, we are*
*essentially very similar. We are all embodied as humans, and we*
*are more alike than we are different. I find comfort in knowing*
*this.*

*I no longer need to be special.*
*I no longer need to stand out from the crowd.*
*I no longer need to be perfect or the best.*

*Now I find plenty of happiness and contentment*
*in the simple tasks of daily life,*
*in sharing, in loving, in mutual commitment,*
*and in knowing that we are all in this (embodied life) together.*

# yoga

# 2

If your goal is evolved embodiment, you must think of your body, mind, and self as a potential artistic masterpiece in the works. Your task, your duty, is to slowly shave away the impurities and rework the texture, reweave the fabric, and reshape the structure to achieve a brilliant and substantiated work of art. The most amazing thing about evolved embodiment is its capacity to have a positive effect on the individual self while simultaneously supporting that individual's harmonious efforts and peaceful presence in the world around her.

Embodiment is a three-dimensional adventure in consciousness, and yoga postures are practical vehicles for molding, shaping, and evolving our embodied consciousness in a way that is both creative and scientific. Using yoga, you are able to explore the many aspects of your Self through an introspective interaction with the medium of the body. How you carry your body, how you move, and the characteristic amount of tension or energy that you transmit or contain in your body are all aspects of your embodiment.

As you learn to tolerate the stillness and silence of a yoga pose, you will begin to tap into subtle bodily sensations that you had previously overlooked. Because these bodily sensations are a physical manifestation that mirrors your mental realm, you can depend on your body to provide accurate and informative material that will help identify the characteristic tendencies, attitudes, and behaviors that you express through posture and movement.

It's easy to see how yoga improves your body's tone and flexibility, but the more significant and esoteric benefits of practicing yoga will only be found through long term practice. It takes commitment to regular practice sessions if you want to develop the capacity for enhanced somatic awareness and gain access to the more sophisticated and sublime somatic information that permeates the depths of the mind-body connection.

When you first attempt any yoga posture, you will immediately notice the general areas of physical discomfort as you try to fit your body into the shape of the pose. You will notice which muscles seem tight, and which body parts seem to be holding you back from going further into the pose. You will notice that, for one reason or another, you are not completely comfortable in the pose. With consistent practice, you will begin to identify specific tensions and localized areas of habitual holding in your body. No doubt you will be surprised to discover that many of these tensions can be quickly and consciously released, and that the process of identifying localized tension in the body is, in many cases, harder than the process of eliminating it. But soon enough you will probably be even more surprised to discover that these localized tensions, which seemed to resolve so quickly and easily, are actually quite persistent - and have returned!

They have returned because they are habitual, which means that they typically exist on a level that lies beyond the conscious mind. This is why it takes a long time to get good at doing yoga. It takes a long time because it is quite unlikely and highly uncommon for long term issues of embodiment (such as ailments or neuroses that originated during childhood trauma) to be resolved quickly, easily, and absolutely.

With this realization, and perhaps with resignation, we begin to understand that the practice of yoga is an evolutionary process that cannot be rushed. Yoga, in its original and most traditional incarnation, is not about perfecting the shape of each pose. It is much more than that. It is a psycho-somatic process of self discovery and conscious evolution. It is a process of evolved embodiment in which your habits, those unconscious behavioral and cognitive processes of which you are normally unaware, are brought to the attention of your conscious mind. Yoga is a process of identifying and scrutinizing the characteristic features of your embodiment, and then consciously deciding if these habits and ways of being should be rejected or retained. If the habits are deemed 'bad' or are in any way self-destructive, they must be replaced by good habits that have a life-affirming effect on the body and mind.

The problem is that habits of any type are hard to identify and harder to change. Even if you want to, you cannot instantly acquire a new, improved version of your body, mind, and Self. You cannot change your habits with a snap of your fingers or the blink of an eye. The reality of embodiment doesn't work that way. It took a period of time for you to acquire, accept, and recognize the present status of your embodiment as Self, and it will take a period of time to change it. Have patience. Have faith.

Yoga is a highly effective body-oriented protocol that will facilitate any type of therapeutic work. Accordingly, the fifteen postures in this yoga program provide a gentle, supportive, and reflective mind-body pathway toward self-awareness, self-acceptance, recovery, rehabilitation and reconnection. Hold still in each pose for about ten slow, steady breaths as you try to get a generalized 'embodied understanding' for the conceptual basis of the pose.

1. Mountain Pose – Am I able to stand alone? Can I take care of myself?

2. Tree Pose – Can I maintain my balance and equanimity at all times?

3. Warrior Pose – Am I able to withstand confrontations and challenges?

4. Triangle Pose - Can I interact with others safely, appropriately, and genuinely? Can I create and sustain satisfying relationships?

5. Gate Pose - Have I established appropriate boundaries and am I able to maintain them?

6. Hero Pose - Am I willing and able to support others if they need my help?

## 7. Table Pose
– Do I feel
adequately supported
and connected?

## 8. Down Dog Pose
– Do I allocate and
manage my time and
resources wisely?

## 9. Boat Pose
– Can I
avoid
distractions
and stay
focused on
the task at
hand?

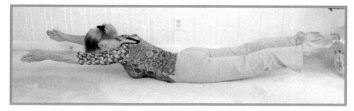

10. Cobra Pose – Am I aware of my situation and surroundings at all times? Am I aware of what is going on around me?

11. Child Pose – Do I feel safe and secure enough to release my vigilance?

12. Dolphin Pose – Can I navigate unusual situations (that are provocative, unfamiliar, or potentially harmful) in a safe and successful way?

13. Seated forward fold
Pose – Can I persevere until
I succeed?

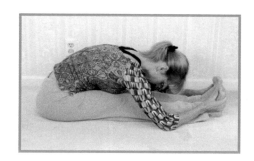

14. Twist Pose – Am I
willing and able to see
things from different
perspectives (without
sacrificing integrity or
safety)?

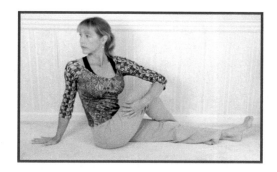

15. Corpse Pose
- Am I able to relax
and be completely at
ease, comfortable and
content?

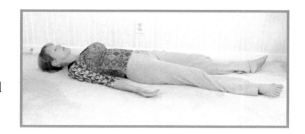

*powerful as a*
# tiger

Some of the yoga postures teach us to be powerful and capable of effective action. These poses are designed to increase energy expenditure by activating or awakening energy. Active poses develop our assertive nature. They help us develop strength, stability, fortitude, courage, confidence, self-reliance, and will power. They help us build physical and mental resources that can be used for protection or defense. The Tiger poses require a moderate to high exertion level.

The psychological lessons are learning to meet a challenge with interest, confidence, and perseverance, to develop problem solving skills, and to make wise choices when faced with fear or aggression. The somatic lessons are learning to rally, harness, and direct energy, as well as to dissipate excessive energy. The Tiger represents the powerful energy flow of the body's backside.

The poses that cultivate our Tiger energy include the Warrior, Triangle, Down Dog, Boat, Cobra, and Dolphin.

*gentle as a*
# lamb

Some of the yoga postures teach us to be gentle, calm, compassionate, and thoughtful. These poses are designed to reduce or stabilize energy expenditure, to contain energy, or to conserve energy. Passive poses develop our tranquil nature. They help us develop a balance between rational, creative and intuitive aspects of consciousness. The Lamb poses require a mild to moderate exertion level.

The psychological lessons are learning to monitor and manage excitement (levels of stimulation and stress) and to maintain equanimity. The somatic lessons are learning to direct and channel energy usage in the most efficient, economical and appropriate way. This is accomplished by reducing the tendency toward scattered, frenzied, or overly ambitious behaviors.

The Lamb represents the nourishing and life-affirming qualities of the body's internal organs. When these organs are functioning harmoniously and peacefully, they will produce optimal health and well being.

The poses that cultivate our Lamb energy include the Tree, Gate, Hero, Table, Seated forward fold, and Twist.

*free as a*
# butterfly

Some of these yoga postures help us to be restored or renewed, and to metaphorically be reborn. Restorative poses are designed to rebuild energy reserves or to allow energy to flow. These poses require a low to moderate exertion level. The somatic lesson is learning to rest, recover, recuperate, and release (let go). The psychological lesson is learning to love and accept all aspects of your self. This is accomplished in conjunction with reducing or eliminating the tendencies toward depletion, withdrawal, and perfectionism. The Butterfly represents a metamorphosis. It represents patience and faith in the process of potential unfolding and awakening. The Butterfly knows that her blossoming, her true beauty, and her ability to fly will come in time. The poses that cultivate our Butterfly energy include the Mountain, Child, and Corpse.

## Yoga Postures

# mountain

Key lesson: Self care

Mind-body lesson: Aspiration to transcendence begins with being grounded in embodiment.

- Teaches basic somatic awareness
- Teaches proper weight distribution
- Teaches grounding
- Teaches centering
- Challenges your sense of balance and symmetry
- Teaches dignity and confidence to stand up for your self

How to do it:
1. Stand with your feet together.
2. Stack your pelvis, thorax, and head.
3. Roll your shoulders down your back.
4. Firm your thighs by pressing the outer thighs inward and the frontal thighs backward.
5. Press your heels into the floor and let your head float upward.
6. Hold the pose for 5 – 10 steady breaths.

## *Affirmation*
I stand up for myself. I can take care of myself.
I am confident in my own abilities.

The Yoga Teacher says: "When you are practicing yoga the focus is exclusively on you. It's all about your body, your thoughts, and your overall experience. Even though, on the surface, this seems to be a selfish perspective, if we look deeper, we will find that the purpose of yoga is ultimately altruistic. Yes, we practice yoga for self improvement. But we do so with the intent of becoming a better individual so that we will have a positive impact on the world around us."

# mountain

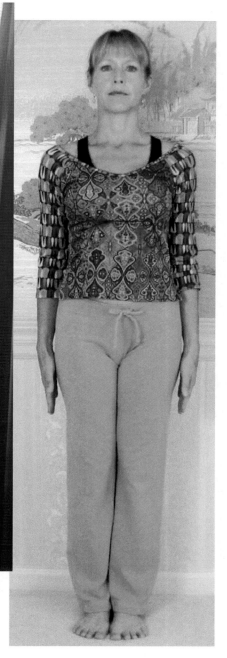

# tree

Key lesson: Self control
Physical lesson: Balance

- Teaches alignment and balance
- Strengthens the muscles in your hip, ankle and foot
- Teaches alignment of the three primary weights
  (pelvis, thorax, head)

How to do it:
1. Start in Mountain pose.
2. Place the sole of your right foot against your left inner thigh.
3. Make prayer hands at the heart.
4. Hold the pose for 5 – 10 steady breaths.
5. Then do the other side.

## *Affirmation*
I maintain my balance and equanimity at all times.

Balance is not just a single point. There is always an acceptable range of balance. Because circumstances are always changing and evolving, maintaining balance requires a conscious readjustment. In the Tree pose, breathing and circulation cause slight movements which must be attended to if we are to maintain balance. The imagery of deep roots that reach from your heels to the center of the Earth will support a solid foundation.

The Yoga Teacher says:
"You can't really stand
on two feet until you can
stand on one foot. You
must trust your foot and
ankle."

tree

# warrior

Key lesson: Self reliance
Physical lesson: Stability

- Challenges the muscles in your hips, legs and feet
- Tones the muscles in your shoulders and trunk

How to do it:
1. Start in the Mountain pose.
2. Step forward with your right foot into a high lunge.
3. Align your right knee directly above the right ankle.
4. Keep your hips squared forward.
5. Keep your left leg (back leg) strong and straight.
6. Lift your arms up alongside your ears, with the palms facing in.
7. Hold the pose for 5 – 10 steady breaths.
8. Then do the other side.

## *Affirmation*
I can withstand confrontations and challenges.

*Heart of the Warrior*

I have a mission.
It is a peaceful mission.
But if I need to,
I will defend myself.
And I will survive.

The Yoga Teacher says, "Detachment means that you will not let the situation provoke, control, bother, belittle, or aggrandize you. If you can learn to remain detached from overwhelming or inappropriate emotional involvement, you will remain steady, stable, calm and centered."

warrior

# triangle

Key Lesson: Personal safety
Symbolism: Dependency, interdependency, and interaction.

- Tones the muscles in your trunk, neck, hips, legs, arms
- Challenges the flexibility of your hips and spine

How to do it:
1. Separate your feet into a wide standing straddle stance.
2. Raise both arms straight out from the shoulders, with the palms facing down.
3. Turn your right foot 90 degrees to the right. Turn your left heel 45 degrees to the left.
4. As you inhale, reach your left hip to the left while stretching your right arm to the right.
5. As you exhale, fold your torso over the right leg and bring the arms to a vertical placement.
6. Turn your head and look up.
7. Hold the pose for 5 – 10 steady breaths.
8. Then do the other side.

## *Affirmation*
I make connections and relationships without losing or relinquishing a sense of my personal control.

The Yoga Teacher says:
"If you think that you cannot do something, stop and think about all of the other people throughout time and history that have been able to do this thing. If all of these people could do it, it is likely that you will be able to do it, too.

triangle

# gate

Key lesson: Boundaries

- Challenges the flexibility of your hips and spine
- Tones your flanks (sides of your waist)

How to do it:
1. Begin in a kneeling position.
2. Shift your weight onto the left knee.
3. Extend your right leg straight out to the right side.
4. Bend to the left, and place your left hand on the floor.
5. Aim the left hand and fingers to the left.
6. Stretch the right arm above your head, reaching away from the right foot.
7. Hold the pose for 5 – 10 steady breaths.
8. Then do the other side.

## *Affirmation*
I establish and maintain appropriate boundaries.

The Yoga Teacher says:

"Find an appropriate balance between receiving and giving back."

gate

# hero

Key lesson: Tolerance
Physical lesson: Perseverance
Psychological lesson: Compassion

- Challenges the joints of your lower extremities
  – feet, ankles, knees, hips

How to do it:
1. Start in a kneeling position.
2. Sit your buttocks down onto your heels.
3. Keep the spine erect.
4. Rest your hands in your lap and look forward at eye level.
5. For a harder variation, turn the toes under.
6. Hold for 5 – 10 steady breaths.

## *Affirmation*
I support others if they need my help.

The Yoga Teacher says: "We all make mistakes. Don't beat yourself up over your mistakes. Sometimes we need to do the wrong thing to be able to see what the right thing really is. Making mistakes is a good way to learn. One of the best ways to grow is to forgive others for the mistakes that they have made."

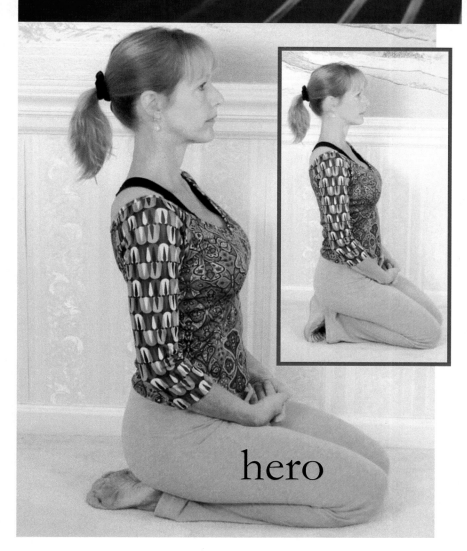

hero

# table

Key Lesson: Connections

Learning concepts:
- Weight distribution
- Grounding down (instead of lifting up)
- Working with gravity

How to do it:
1. Start on the ground in a hands and knees position.
2. Spread your fingers and push your hands against the floor.
3. Look down at the floor between your hands.
4. Extend your right leg straight back and lift it to hip height.
5. Extend your left arm forward and lift it to shoulder height.
6. Hold the pose for 5 – 10 steady breaths.
7. Then do the other side.

## *Affirmation*
I feel supported and connected.

The Yoga Teacher says:
"As long as you are living life as a human,
your body is your home."

# table

# down dog

Key lesson: Real time (a feature of mindfulness)

- Experience the length and width of your back
- Stretches the whole backside of the body
- Strengthens the shoulders

How to do it:
1. Start on the ground in a hands and knees position.
2. Align your hands under your shoulders, and align your knees under your hips.
3. Lift your hips upward and backward, away from your hands.
4. Aim your tailbone up. (Avoid hanging in the shoulders.)
5. Press your heels toward the floor.
6. Drop your head down and look at your toes.
7. Hold the pose for 5 – 10 steady breaths.

## *Affirmation*
I allocate and manage my time and resources wisely.

The Yoga Teacher says:
"Try your best without trying too hard."

# down dog

# boat

Key lesson: Mental acuity (a feature of mindfulness)

- Strengthens the musculature on the whole backside of your body
- Teaches the concept of a bodily central channel

How to do it:
1. Begin in a prone position, resting on your forehead with your arms extended forward.
2. As you inhale, lift your head a few inches off the floor.
3. At the same time, lift your arms and legs.
4. Keep your kneecaps facing down.
5. Press your ribcage and pelvis into the floor.
6. Avoid hunching or tightening your shoulders.
7. Hold the pose for 5 – 10 steady breaths.

## *Affirmation*
I can avoid distractions. I can stay focused on the task at hand.

The Yoga Teacher says: "When you are practicing yoga, always assume that you are doing it right. Don't tell yourself that you are wrong. But at the same time, remain open to the possibility that there might be a better way. Always be willing to explore, to change, and to improve, for you are likely to discover a way that is even more right."

boat

# cobra

Key lesson: Situational awareness (a feature of mindfulness)

- Challenges the flexibility of your spine
- Strengthens the muscles in your back
- Helps improve your posture

How to do it:
1. Begin in a prone position with your forehead on the floor and your hands positioned under your shoulders.
2. As you inhale, slowly lift your head up, facing forward.
3. Press down into the hands as you continue to lift the spine upwards.
4. Either straighten the arms or keep them bent at a 45 degree angle.
5. Focus on pressing the thoracic spine forward into your body.
6. Keep the shoulders down and the elbows held in.
7. Hold the pose for 5 -10 steady breaths.

## *Affirmation*

I am aware of my situation and surroundings at all times.
I am safe.

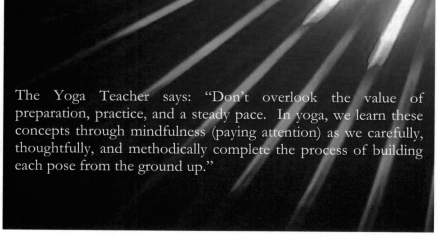

The Yoga Teacher says: "Don't overlook the value of preparation, practice, and a steady pace. In yoga, we learn these concepts through mindfulness (paying attention) as we carefully, thoughtfully, and methodically complete the process of building each pose from the ground up."

cobra

# child

Key lesson: Trust

- Challenges the hips, knees, ankles, and feet
- Opportunity for rest and relaxation

How to do it:
1. Begin in a kneeling position.
2. Sit your bottom down onto your heels.
3. Lower your chest onto your thighs and place your forehead on the floor.
4. Fold your arms under your head OR let your arms rest alongside your body, with the palms facing up.
5. Soften your elbows and relax your shoulders.
6. Relax your jaw.
7. Hold the pose for 5 – 10 steady breaths.

## *Affirmation*
I release my vigilance because I am safe and secure.

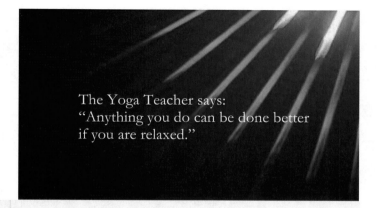

The Yoga Teacher says:
"Anything you do can be done better
if you are relaxed."

child

The Yoga Teacher says:
"You are the expert on what
you are feeling in your own body."

# dolphin

Key lesson: Self reliance

- Reverses circulation (due to inversion)
- Challenges arm and shoulder strength

How to do it:
1. Begin in a kneeling position.
2. Lean forward and place the crown of your head on the floor.
3. Clasp your hands together and hold your head.
4. Lift up onto your toes and straighten your legs.
5. Lift your heels high, and look back at your toes.
6. Hold the pose for 5 – 10 steady breaths.

## Affirmation:
I navigate unusual or difficult situations safely and successfully.

The Yoga Teachers says: "In yoga there is no need for comparison or competition. There is no room for judgment. Yoga is an individualized practice, which means that each person works at her own level. Ultimately, each person is learning to do what is best for her in present time."

dolphin

# seated forward fold

Key lesson: Managing energy (energy conservation)

- Stretches the muscles in the backside of your body
- Opportunity to experience surrender (letting go of neediness and desires) and emotional release

How to do it:
1. Begin in a seated position with your legs straight forward.
2. Keep your back straight.
3. As you inhale, raise your arms up alongside your ears.
4. As you exhale, slowly fold forward from the hips, reaching your arms forward.
5. When you can't go any further forward, release your arms and drop your head.
6. Keep the outer thighs pressing inward and the frontal thighs pressing backward. Keep your feet flexed.
7. Hold the pose for 5 – 10 steady breaths.

## *Affirmation*
I can persevere until I succeed.

The Yoga Teacher says: "Paradoxically, sometimes what seems right might be exactly what is wrong. Don't assume that what you think is right is written in stone. At higher levels of consciousness, right and wrong are concepts of relativity.

# seated forward fold

# twist

Key lesson: Managing energy (directing energy)

Psychological symbolism: Looking back into the past is no longer traumatic.

- Unwinds and adjusts the spine
- Releases tightness in the spinal column
- Stretches the buttocks and hips

How to do it:
1. Begin in a seated position with your legs extended forward.
2. Bend the left leg and place the left foot flat on the floor outside the right thigh.
3. Gently turn your body to the left.
4. Using your right arm, hug the left knee close to your chest.
5. Place your left hand on the floor behind your hips.
6. Rotate from the abdomen while keeping the hips squared. Most of the rotation should occur in the ribcage, shoulders, and neck.
7. Hold the pose for 5 – 10 steady breaths.

## *Affirmation*
I am willing and able to see things from different perspectives.

The Yoga Teacher says: "The pose of the novice yoga student is simplistic because she focuses exclusively on how the pose looks. The accomplished yoga student, on the other hand, brings awareness and refinement to her practice. She has learned that you cannot fully understand an experience if you only observe a singular perspective."

twist

# corpse

Key lesson: Faith

- Learn to relax at will
- Learn to bring your body and mind to stillness
- Experience a few moments of bliss

How to do it:
1. Lie in a supine position.
2. Separate your legs a comfortable distance apart.
3. Separate your arms a comfortable distance away from your body.
4. Close your eyes and bring your attention to the breath.
5. Every time you exhale, relax a little more.
6. Remain in this pose for 3 – 5 minutes or longer.

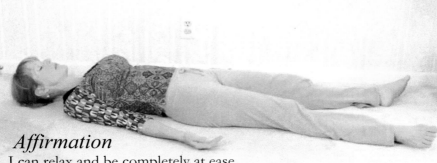

## *Affirmation*
I can relax and be completely at ease.
I am comfortable and content.

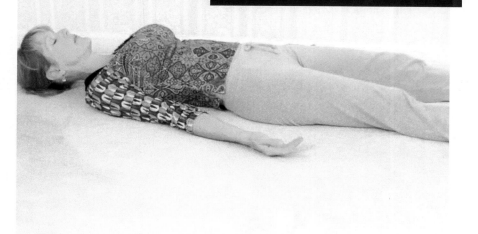

The Yoga Teacher says: "Steady breath, steady mind, relaxed body. You cannot have one without the others. Steady breath, steady mind, relaxed body. These are the indications of a peaceful, blissful state of being. These are the indications of health, happiness, and well-being."

# corpse

# *Yoga*
## is a somatic experience
## of self-discovery

Do not make the mistake of seeking mastery of your body in a yoga pose. Aggression and agenda are never appropriate when practicing yoga. Yoga is a practice, not a performance. It involves somatic education and re-education, and it requires patience, optimism and commitment. If you really want to grow, to be healed, to stay healthy, or to be freed from past trauma, you must stick with it. Both recovery and self-discovery are a long term process. Thankfully, the techniques you learn in yoga will support you through a lifetime.

When you understand what
you are doing and why you are doing it,
you are experiencing mindfulness in action.

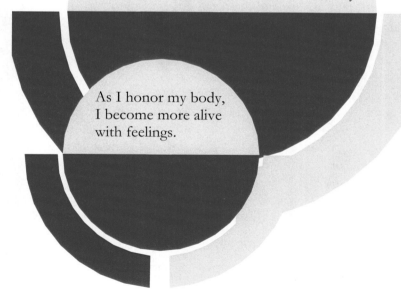

Consciousness must be rooted in the body.

As I honor my body,
I become more alive
with feelings.

# symbolism
*awakening through creativity*

# 3

All of us could benefit from tapping into an effective channel for transpersonal processing and growth. Creativity in any form can provide such a channel. A unique feature found in the creative impulse is symbolism. Symbolism is the practice of representing things by means of symbols, or of attributing symbolic meanings or significance to objects, events, or relationships. Exploring symbolism can help us understand how images and ideas can change our minds.

Contemplating visual art, reflecting on an archetype, and reading creative writing or poetry are all pathways that can produce provocative effects on the psyche. These effects can potentially lead to changes or 'reframing' in terms of perception, perspective, and understanding, and they will be matched by somatic changes in the body. For example, if you look at an image or symbol that depicts gentleness and kindness, the muscles of your face and shoulders will soften and relax.

In this chapter we will explore the use of creativity and symbolism in poetry, art, and short stories. Use this chapter as a foundation for studying the realm of symbolism in the world around you. Try to become more aware of both the obvious and the subliminal effects of how symbolism affects a broader audience, such as strategies used for advertising and imagery that is related to cultural and religious materials. Perhaps even more importantly, begin to notice the specific colors, tastes, scents, sensations, items, places, and memories which are uniquely symbolic and significant to you.

*Majesty* suggests greatness, dignity and royalty. It denotes supreme authority or power. Majesty implies the attributes of splendor and magnificence - in appearance, style, or character. Though majesty denotes a sense of grandeur in terms of image and conduct, it also suggests separation based on rank and social status. Majesty is considered to be above, beyond, or more refined than the common and ordinary. *In this poem, has majesty, in all its glory, brought the author contentment?

## majesty

it has taken a long, long time to reach this point
this high degree of fitness, firmness
endurance, assurance
let it be known, there is no Achilles heel
only a figure to beat the band.
majesty is not the body alone
the fire burns behind the eyes
and now they will stand back and look at me
study me, praise me, some will analyze.
in eyes of wonder and eyes of awe, is it coveting i see?
they look, and i am glad
look me over!
i will stand strong and confident. my posture will show them
how i feel, how i think.
surely, i will meet each eye for eye
poised, i will stand tall and sleek
they can't touch me now
they can't stun me, body or mind
my pedestal is complete.
i've come together in my time, like the Trojan horse
not to be penetrated until i open the door myself
it has taken a period of time to develop
so many years -
but now let them stand back, look up and admire
as i am so tall.

A *tailspin* describes a rapid spiral movement in the tail section of a descending aircraft that appears to be out of control. Psychologically, a tailspin refers to an emotional collapse or loss of emotional control. *In this poem, does the author consider the tailspin to be a positive or negative symbol?

## the tailspin

i'm coming out of a tailspin
and it's so hard to control
the whirling motion
and the wild dives i take
sometimes the beating fan
can be deafening,
though no one else can hear it.
(they hear their own)
i want to put my hands
to my ears
cover them
and with closed eyed, tightly
teeth clenched
stop it, stop it yet
the tailspin takes me down.
will i crash?
blinded, i see swirling
colors and spinning shapes
and nothing and no one comes clear
i can focus on nothing.
endlessly
my kaleidoscope copes.
i'm caught
and a part, ever
coming out of a tailspin
a never ending tailspin
better to constantly come
than be lost lost lost.

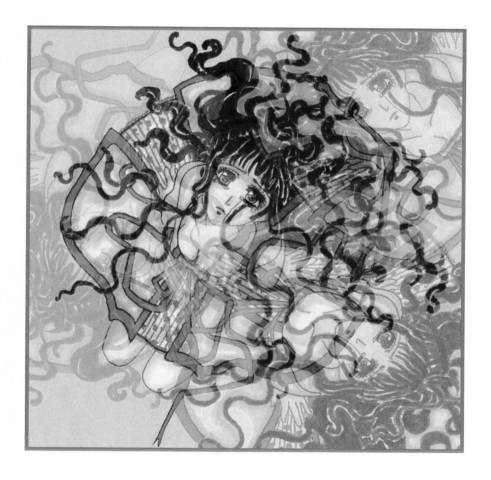

The *crossroads* is an intersection of two paths and an opportunity for choice. Sometimes it is appropriate to change direction and set off on a new adventure with a new destination, but other times it is better to choose commitment and continuity along your present path. The most important thing about a crossroads is that a direction, objective, or course of action must be selected and followed. Only then will the journey continue. *In this poem, is the author's perspective of the crossroads based on monotony or transcendence?

the crossing

i come to the corner
first
alone.
i can see their shadows
as each steps in
behind me.
i see their shadows
standing long and dark.
i can see the bags
they carry
reflected on the street
in front
of us.
the sun lets me watch
as they gather around
and behind me
waiting
i am aware of the sign
flashing white.
one steps forward, and
the others follow.
i do too
moving on along
across.

it is a long way,
it seems,
across
to the other side.
walking, drifting
with the crowd.
aware
but not really seeing
nor hearing
all the traffic around me —
the buses and cars,
the elevated.
all the traffic lights,
policemen
street preachers,
and such.
i carry myself forward
looking straight
ahead.
remotely aware
of all the distractions
playing
on my mind
but
my concentration
is not broken.
i cross in front
passing
them all by
lost in thought.

The *classroom* is a familiar metaphor for life. It is an environment for learning, but it is also a place of testing, judgment, and competition. For many of us, this is why the classroom represents a fearful or threatening place that brings up issues of self-worth and self-doubt.  *In this poem, which part of the classroom experience makes the author feel uncomfortable?

## the classroom

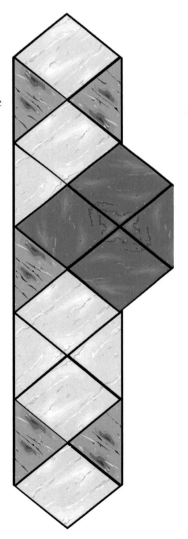

the classroom is proper, and noisy at first
i watch as many pairs of jeans walk by me
silently in my row
some brush my shoulder as they pass
with their bags
occasionally one utters a soft sorry, but
uses it only as social etiquette
and doesn't really care, though i was
fitted into my own seat, careful
to complete only my own space
and it was not my fault,
i am made to feel so.
i sit and look about
me, and still they come
through the door
walking fast and strong, direct
to an open seat, chattering.
i am glad when those around me
are taken, settled in for the hour.

Plugs are typically associated with cords, wires, and switches. In combination, these symbolic images suggest connections that provide a conduit for a power source. These images are a metaphor for relationship, community, interaction, flow, order, direction, and wisdom. To be 'plugged in' is to be in touch, to be in the know. To be 'plugged up' is to be stuck, closed, obstructed, or contained. While *unplugged* typically denotes some sort of disconnection, it can also indicate a state of freedom or release in which problems, blockages and obstacles have been overcome.  *In this poem, what is contained or bound by the plug?

## unplugged

i used to be
plugged.
there were definite
starts and stops
to the day
or the activity
and i was
scared and i was
insecure.
i felt others
watching me
talking about me
and worst of all laughing
at me.
i used to have
windstorms in my head
that mixed up
my thoughts and
limited, obstructed happiness;
no contentment
was freed;
no vegetables
did i eat

yet i thought i knew
what i did.
i thought i lived
like all others
and they were all
against me
but
i was merely plugged up
and that plug
caused imbalance
in me, in all ways.
slowly, somehow
it worked its way out
little by little things
changed
and i really don't
remember
or didn't even notice
when it
happened.
when the plug fell
out the flow came
freely, smoothly,
so peacefully
it all began now
to flow
and they no longer
scared me or
offended me
for i became
more and more
a part of it and them,
and from somewhere
happiness came.

*Putty* is a type of clay-like or cement-like substance that is typically used to fill holes or seal cracks. Its grayish-brown or grayish-yellow color is remarkably bland. The most useful attribute of putty is its pliability - the ability to be molded into a shape or manipulated into a consistency that can fill a particular need. But if it is left alone and not handled for a period of time, putty will grow cold and hard. *In this poem, how is putty used as a metaphor for the victim consciousness?

## putty

i am putty in your hands
you can take me
and mold me
into whatever
you please.
you can make me a princess
in a castle far away
surrounded by clouds
with silver linings, one day
put me in a turret high above the land
and keep me there, guarded
by your protective hand.
you can
make me beautiful, make me strong
teach me patience
i'll never do wrong
all this
you can do
i will be what you want
or with one wrong word
you can reduce
me down to a blob of colorless clay
your putty, your plaything
and throw me away.

A big issue for many of us is *happiness.* We periodically ponder questions like "Am I happy? What would make me happy?" Do you think that happiness is a purely mental construct, or can you feel happiness in your body? If so, what are the sensations of happiness? Does happiness register as energy, intensity, fullness, moderation, warmth, chills, containment, expansion, stillness, movement, firmness, softness? As you read each of the next three poems, become aware of how your body is responding and reacting to the key idea or theme. Do you feel a mutual understanding (an embodied 'gut level' of understanding) with the author's perspective?

## how much happiness?

how much happiness are we allowed in life?
has God allotted
so much per person
and after that amount
is used up
will there be no more?
or
are we held
at regulated levels
a floor and ceiling of happiness.
or maybe
with increased effort can we
reap greater benefits?
if i were to put all my energy
into
achieving goals to bring me happiness,
will the end reward
truly be
happiness
or
merely the goal itself?

we spend our time
chasing rainbows
every day
constantly reaching, searching,
and sorting
the changes in our lives
we analyze feelings and
desires,
and
the question becomes
just what will make me happy?
the wise ones
realize
that the true question is
will we ever know?

## something special

there are times
when i feel
overcome with happiness
by all the special things
we are blessed with
in simple day to day life.
they are too plentiful
to really even begin
to appreciate
as we should.
lucky, we are
lucky, to have
all the opportunities.
so give thanks
and stop to smile
and contemplate
our good fortune
and all the special things.
look, don't miss it —
something special
is always right there
under your nose.

## still, i wonder

still, i wonder
what will happen
what
will tomorrow bring
will i be
happy, sad, carefree, mad
will i feel
pretty, content, and vivacious
or
worthless, unloved
lost in self-despair
will i radiate
or will i pull inward
yes, i wonder
what
tomorrow will bring
but why
do i wonder
when tomorrow will bring
what
it will
and i have no control
over tomorrow
no, i only control
my mind
my feelings
my attitude
all that influences
how the day will be for me
yet i wonder, still
what will happen
when tomorrow comes
but why
for i control
my tomorrows

## journey

is this your mind?
i've never been here,
before.
i see your rainbow thoughts and taste your desires.
your dreams forming and dissolving,
like footprints on the beach
the melodies of your soul
and you, dancing.
you are safe here.
but also lonely,
always.
because no one can see you here
dancing
with no remorse,
no apologies, no self-conscious laughter
but you're still alone.
no one has ever seen you here.
no one knows you.

i see you.
i see what you are,
now.
you're not your gender, age, profession, or color.
you're a human being first,
and only
just like me
just like you.

i see you.
i see your mind
and your soul
for just this moment I see you
i love you
i wish you could see me.

As you read the short story *Crystal's Reflection,* notice its fairy tale qualities. In the beginning, the beautiful, princess-like heroine is wounded. She endures a period of confinement for contemplation, during which she encounters the proverbial 'dark night of the soul.' Discovering the shocking truth of reality, she is transformed. Finally, she emerges from the adventure with a different perspective and a deeper level of understanding. *When the horrific nature of the truth is revealed, does it produce a positive or negative transformation of her character?

# Crystal's Reflection

In the cool days of early spring, Crystal Lancelet hid herself away like a captured princess in her family's great white house, and through this put a great grass lawn and budding trees between herself and the cruel grey school where a classmate had insulted her, because she certainly was not how that girl had described her. And even if she was, just a little, she would soon be cured of it. After all, high up in her glossy tower, there was no one to raise her onto their shoulders, so she was certain she would soon float back down to humble reality.

Even so, her prison was hardly ascetic. It was beautiful, with wide windows that opened to see cherry blossom trees wrapped in great balls of flowery, pink cotton candy. The bathroom, which was accessible only through her bedroom, had always been the secret and sacred heart of her sanctuary. It was unusually large, even to the point that it had its own small closet, and presented a great white bathtub as the center piece.   Crystal would spend her afternoons dancing around the cool, wide open space, her hair sparkling with the refraction of glass figurines, ornaments, and perfume bottles. When she became tired of practicing her footwork, she took long bubble baths as the sheer curtains twirled in the breeze, occasionally letting cherry blossoms drift in onto the clean tile floor. Most of all, she would spend hours sitting on her marble counter staring into a great, expansive mirror, convincing herself that she was as beautiful on the inside as the palace that she had locked herself away in.

"She really had no right to say it, even to suggest it at all." She would tell herself, little by little forgetting what she had actually been accused of, while turning her head to different angles, making sure she was flawlessly gorgeous from all sides. "I mean, honestly, how could she find any fault in me?" Even at night, when the air was as black as ink, she would slip out of her crisp, clean bed to stare into the mirror. At times, in the darkness, she would blindly reach out her hand to touch the mirror, and felt, or thought she felt, not the cold hard sting of glass, but the cool, lively touch of a human hand. And when she stared into the pitch black mirror, she felt as though someone was staring back, and it excited and aroused her.

Crystal had not talked to her friends in weeks, and left the house only when she had to. She spent hours, days, staring into that mirror in a half trance, thinking how perfect she was. Sometimes, she was sure that she was the one sitting on the other side of the glass watching the real Crystal. She was half insane with love of herself, and thought it was perfectly normal when it felt like she was following her reflection's lead, and later, when her reflection seemed to speak in a sweet, refreshing voice with dancing words of praise for her beauty. But then she would shiver, and the reflection was again nothing more than her image in the mirror. However, she missed that sweet voice.

One day, after a month of isolation and nearly a day of staring into her own eyes, Crystal was as deep in as she had ever been, feeling nothing but the cool breeze and countertop, hearing nothing but that sweet voice, and thinking nothing except hoping, vaguely, that this could go on forever. And a little excited by the idea that it could, with one touch, just one sweet embrace . . .

A car horn blasted through the window from a passing truck. Crystal startled, and for a moment, just two seconds, she saw a horrible thing. Her reflection, halfway through a sentence, was staring back at her with the most evil, devilish grin she had ever seen, and, to her absolute shock, had somehow reached out of the mirror and had grabbed her with both arms. Shrieking, she pushed away and fell backwards off the countertop. When she stood up a moment later, all she saw was her shocked expression staring back at her. Still, she knew what she had seen and she would not go near the mirror. That car horn, that rusty old car horn that blasted out from a burning, busted-up engine had broken her from the crisp, cool grasp of her keeper, and she, with a hot, beating heart, was afraid.

She ran from her prison, out of her room and down the hall toward the stairs she fled, carefully avoiding the glance of any mirror she might pass, fearing that it might somehow follow her. At the top of the stairs, she found, to her surprise, something that would have met with only her scorn not five minutes before. It was a hammer, a wooden, worn hammer, sturdy and reliable with many years of faithful toil, and had most likely been left there by her father, who had finally gotten around to fixing that banister. Not sure what she was doing, but knowing that as long as she left that great mirror intact she was leaving open a door for that thing, that horrible thing that had tried to stupefy her into complacency. Crystal entered her white sanctuary brandishing a workman's hammer and smashed the mirror before she even had a chance to look into it. Relieved, she dropped the hammer on the floor next to the glass bits and tried to catch her breath.

"Oh, now look what a mess you've made." Shocked by the voice, Crystal looked down in horror to see her own face staring in a harsh rage back at her, and, even worse, it had managed to reach its arm out of one of the larger shards of glass and was feeling around for the hammer, which lay only inches away. "How would you feel if someone did that to you, huh?" it yelled, brandishing the hammer. Crystal ran for her closet and was able to get behind the door just as the hammer hit it with a heavy thud that shook its frame.

Peeping out from behind the door, Crystal saw the sharp metal end of the hammer thoroughly imbedded in the middle of the door. Looking at the floor, she saw that her reflection was attempting to hastily reassemble itself by using its three dimensional arm to slide the pieces of glass back into their proper places. Panicking, Crystal attempted to pull the hammer out of the door, but it was thoroughly stuck. Meanwhile, the ghastly hand was making much headway. Desperate and seeing no alternative, Crystal jumped onto the broken glass with her bare feet. She continued to stomp on all the pieces of the broken mirror, working through the pain of the broken shards in her soles, until there wasn't a fragment of glass left big enough for even a finger to get through, and the tiles were red with blood from her feet. In extreme pain, she maneuvered herself onto her marble counter, now with nothing behind her but an empty wall, and washed her bloody feet in the sink.   By the time the heat of summer had settled in, Crystal's feet had healed, and she had returned much to the way her friends had remembered her with only a few new quirks. She refused, absolutely refused, to be alone in a bathroom, and loathed to look at herself in a compact mirror. However, from the time that she had returned, no one had accused her, or even thought of accusing her, of being too in love with herself.

In the short story *Rosalyn and Delilah,* we witness a relationship between two sisters. *Which sister do you identify with? Does this story prompt any sibling-related memories from your childhood?

# Rosalyn and Delilah

Rosalyn Wallace had always been very suspicious of her little sister and for the sole reason that Delilah was disgustingly, majestically, and radiantly new and different from the bitterly self-conscious first born. When Rosalyn got a glass of water, she would put no ice in it at all, and drink it all at once but with no great speed. With every swallow, she could see a wave travel out of her mouth and to the far end of the glass destined to inevitably return, and when it did she would swallow it and release another, smaller wave. When she was done, she would look through the bottom of the glass at the lamps and silverware and watch the sunbeams refract until she could see tiny rainbows in the water drops still clinging to the inverted bottom. Of course, she saved such luxuries for when she was alone. The world and her parents wouldn't understand, and even if they would, she didn't want them to. Delilah, on the other hand, would fill her cup up with so much ice that it was a wonder that there was any room left for water at all. She would then, perhaps following the example of her sister, drink all the water, but because she couldn't see the waves through all the ice, she would just drain the glass as quickly as her little throat could swallow it. Then, of course, that great pile of ice, which looks like nothing less than a mountain when you are a five year old staring up through a glass, would collapse in a great avalanche onto her tiny nose. Through the great pile of ice, Delilah could look up and see rainbows and yellow sunbeams everywhere with everything cold. Beyond the glass sky above the ice mountain was a warm kitchen with lots of twinkling lights and a smiling mother with big brown eyes who would laugh, call her silly, carefully remove the glass and its ice so that none spilled on the floor, and wipe her chilled nose with a dishrag so that little Delilah didn't wander through life with a frosty nose. Delilah laughed and giggled when she was called silly and her mother wiped her nose because she was five and not nine like Rosalyn, who was bitterly self-conscious, only looked through the empty glass when she was all alone, and was always very suspicious of her little sister because deep down in her glass heart she harbored a feeling that her parents loved her little sister more than they did her, and worse, that they were in fact entirely correct in who they chose to bestow their love.

Later on, the family bought a new refrigerator that dispensed water as well as ice, but because the water was cold it somehow fused the ice cubes together as soon as it hit them. From then on, whenever Delilah drained her cup the giant block of ice would just slide down and bob her in the nose instead of burying her. It is usually in this or in similar fashions that all which was great and majestic in childhood disappears. Eventually she gave the practice up entirely and started putting no ice in her water, like Rosalyn. This, of course, aggravated Rosalyn to no end because the one thing worse than having someone do something new and different is to have them do exactly what you do when all you want in the world is to be the only you in it.

Because Mr. and Mrs. Wallace both had jobs, the girls sometimes had to spend their summer days with Mrs. Iyler, the nice lady who was younger than their mother and lived in the apartment down the hall with her husband, Mr. Iyler, who was never at home when Rosalyn and Delilah were there, a baby named Michael, three cats, and a goldfish. One pities the goldfish.

Sometimes Mrs. Iyler would get out an old ice-cream maker, and she, Delilah, and the baby (who really did nothing at all) would make ice cream to have in the afternoons. However, because Rosalyn was ten, and not five like Delilah, she never helped with the ice cream and didn't eat much of it either, because she was getting to that age that she knew if she ever wanted to have a lot of friends she would have to be very, very thin. Of course, she was already very, very thin, and she didn't have many friends, while Delilah, who was small and chubby for her age, was loved by everyone. But Rosalyn knew that there was a big difference between being five, short for your age, and chubby, and being ten, the tallest girl in your class, and chubby. So, for that reason, Rosalyn decided to stay thin and lanky like she was, although she was still a little skeptical that a person really had any power to change the way they looked or anything else about themselves. Still, she ate the ice cream when they made strawberry, because that was her favorite flavor, but pretended she didn't like it at all and only ate it as a favor to Delilah, who always worked very hard on it with the single minded determination of someone who was still naïve to the real world.

One time, later during that sleepy, peaceful summer that had so far been plagued only by holidays and birthdays, Rosalyn was riding her bike along the street, while Mrs. Iyler, Delilah, and the baby sat outside blowing bubbles that came in a little jar. They were having such a wonderful time that they almost forgot that a very tasty goldfish was currently alone in a room with three very hungry cats. A cat considers it below its dignity to show that it is hungry by anything more obvious than the telltale signs of occasionally licking its whiskers and watching the goldfish with lazy but intrigued attention. The goldfish, which had no greater desire in life than to be safe in his little glass of water, quickly dived behind his little plastic castle as soon as the first cat's paw dipped beneath the surface.

Rosalyn skidded on the road and fell off her bike as a car sped past. Her right knee was scraped up pretty good, and her right palm was torn up a bit. There was hot blood on the hot pavement. Mrs. Iyler helped Rosalyn over to the sidewalk, told her to stay right there, and she hurried up to the apartment to get a cloth and some disinfectant. The baby starting crying and there were hot tears on red cheeks. Rosalyn wanted to cry too but she was ten and not six so she certainly wasn't going to let Delilah see her sobbing even though it hurt really badly. She held her knee with her left hand but the right hand hurt if she held it against anything so she just had to leave it out in space where even the air made it sting. Delilah asked if it hurt, Rosalyn said yes, it felt like it was burning. She kept her head down because she didn't want Delilah to see the tears, but when she glanced up Delilah was gone and she was all alone on the burning sidewalk with a burning hand and a screaming red baby.

Seconds later, she heard running footsteps coming back toward her, and a moment after that her bloody hand was grabbed by tiny hands and pressed inside a wet cloth saturated with cold water. It stung worse at first, so she tried to pull away, but the little hands held firm and soon it began to feel much better. After a while Delilah let go of Rosalyn's hand and pressed the bottom of her sundress, with had once been clean with crisp blue and white stripes and little decorative flowers at the hem, but was now crumpled, soaking wet, and red with blood, to Rosalyn's knee.

Delilah, who was only six and not ten, didn't know much about injuries or blood, but she did know that burning was caused by fire, and that a good glass of cold water could solve anything, that it was all anybody every really needed, be it goldfish or girl. So she ran to the garden hose behind the building and sprayed her dress with ice cold water because she had no other way to get it back to her sister. Before that moment, Delilah had really loved that dress. She loved that dress, and everybody knew it. That's why, when Mrs. Iyler finally got back down the three flights of stairs with the disinfectant and saw the three children sitting there all in tears, she thought of Delilah's bloody dress just a moment before she thought of Rosalyn's bloody knee. Everyone loves Delilah, but Delilah loved Rosalyn even more than her lovely dress.

The dress was ruined as red, white and blue turned to brown, white and blue and it became obvious that the stains, the life blood of a sister, weren't going to come out, could never be washed away. However, the goldfish was still alive, so it was sort of a half victory for the day.

That night, their parents got home, and Rosalyn received pity kisses for being hurt and almost being hit by a car, and Delilah received good girl and sympathy kisses for thinking of her sister and losing her dress, which she used to love very much but was already beginning to forget about. Rosalyn lay in her top bunk and felt her knee still sting a little, under the cotton, bandage tape, and two blankets. She wondered if her blood would ever come back. She was too lanky to bleed. It poured out so easily, too easily. There wasn't a lot in her to start with. She had been made a glass half full, and with no ice at all. She couldn't afford to lose anything, not like Delilah. Delilah had been made overflowing, with water, with life, and with blood. Rosalyn thought how it wasn't fair, that she was made with so little when Delilah was made with so much. Delilah, who had more, could have hoarded it all away and left people in blood on the sidewalk but instead gave freely. Rosalyn knew she would be selfish if she had it all. She would keep it hidden and savor it herself sip by sip. Delilah really was the better girl. Perhaps the world was right in who they chose to give their love.

But if Delilah was free to choose, then so was Rosalyn.

Rosalyn, quietly in the darkness, pushed back the covers and climbed down the ladder by her bed, even though her knee hurt when it bent, even though her hand hurt when it grabbed the rungs of the ladder. She went to the kitchen, pulled a glass out of the cupboard, and took it to the refrigerator. A light when on and the whole kitchen seemed to be cast in a glow as ice filled the cup, all the way up to the brim. Then the water was poured from the sink so that it wasn't so cold that it would bind the ice. It was all pointless anyway. The ice would all be melted by the time Delilah woke up in the morning. And Rosalyn hated doing pointless things, but she did it anyway because it didn't feel so pointless. She put the water on the dresser next to Delilah's bed and climbed the ladder, her knee smarting horribly the whole time, and she was pretty sure that it had started bleeding anew. Rosalyn climbed into bed, turned toward the wall, waited for her knee to stop stinging, and then went to sleep.

The next morning, when Delilah woke up, there were tiny rainbows and bright lights all over the walls where the morning sun was refracting off the glass of water by her bed. Delilah was happy, but she didn't sit up or get out of bed because she was six and not ten, and she knew that her sister would be very angry if she woke her up early, even for this.

# visual art
*aesthetics and inspiration*

# 4

Visual art is considered a transformative medium and creative method that is especially useful during life transitions and the process of recovery. Art can affect us. Art can influence us by modifying bits and pieces of our ever-evolving personal style and sense of self through the intuitive appreciation of aesthetics.

Use the artwork in this book as a creative channel to inspire your actions, to awaken your heart, to spark your creativity, to enlarge your outlook, to help you identify and support your purpose, and to have a positive impact on your journey. This chapter is specifically designed to help you appreciate and embrace the glory of the feminine aspect of consciousness.

Pause to reflect on each piece of artwork and the brief statement of 'contemplation' or 'affirmation' that accompanies it. Study the details of each piece and look for symbolism. Then notice the sensations that arise from within your body. What do these sensations mean? What do they represent? As you look at each image, how do you respond? How does this image affect you? Do you feel comfortable and at ease? Do you feel angry or unsure? Do you feel an affinity for this image? Do you feel shocked by this image? Do you feel attuned?

We live in a society that identifies feminine beauty through strict standards of vanity and appearance.

*I often feel pressured by the drive for perfection, success, power and control. But as I have begun to awaken, I wonder if these drives might be compensation strategies. Sometimes I suspect that these drives conceal an unconscious longing for love, acceptance, and contentment. Somewhere deep inside myself, I know that these drives are unsubstantiated and impure.*

*I have a yearning.*
*I have a longing for sustenance and satisfaction.*
*I am in search of meaning.*

*My awareness must be grounded in embodied human reality, so that I can relate to the divine without identifying with it. I walk the life of a human, but I understand that there is a deeper, sublime quality to my existence.*

*My soul is crying out for life. She is carefully and steadily making her way to the surface. She is gradually becoming brighter, clearer, stronger, and more radiant. I can almost hear her calling out "I am here. I am now. I am."*

*To find my own story, I must assemble all the parts of myself. What is my life about? How are my wounds significant to me? Do I recognize parts of my self in others? Do I recognize parts of others in my self?*

*I appreciate and value nourishment. I dress and behave with expression and ease. I cherish my family and friends.*

*I love and accept both the light and dark aspects of myself. Essentially, I am a divine being, but for right now, I am living a human life.*

*I like, love, and approve of myself.*

# amaterasu's attributes

*integrity*

*harmony*

*balance and grace*

*order*

*clarity*

I aspire to be like she who shines in the heavens

*conclusion*
# mind-body expansion

When someone has a narrow-minded perspective we say that she has a closed mind. This means that she is not willing to consider the value or validity of different viewpoints. Due in large part to our childhood indoctrination, we all carry this type of close-minded baggage. For example, if your parents looked down on anyone who smoked, drank, was overweight, or owned a dog, you grew up believing that people who did these things were bad. But you were mistaken, for these were only viewpoints, not facts. These viewpoints were simply beliefs that belonged to your parents.

Metaphorically, a closed mind is 'constipating' because it holds firmly to what it believes and is not capable of accepting additional input, proper processing or elimination. A closed mind is a rigid mind, and it is associated with a tense body. Tension, which is the byproduct of bodily contraction, limits or reduces the body's capacity for movement on all levels – circulation, digestion, elimination, joint range of motion, quality and quantity of respiration, and the capabilities of sensory receptors. A closed mind and a tense body are suffering from the containment syndrome, which stifles the free flow of the body's life affirming processes.

To be healed and healthy, we need to open up. Openness is closely related to acceptance and expansion, and it creates space for possibilities. In a literal sense, our physical (bodily) goal is to restore adequate space inside our bodies to support better breathing, better digestion, and optimal movement. Figuratively, openness improves the mental realm by making space for new ideas, new adventures, new understandings, and new perspectives. Open mindedness is about graciously considering the unconventional and unfamiliar.

For example, instead of defining yourself in terms of boundaries and confinement by asking "What can't I do?" or stating "I could never do that," ask yourself "What can I do?" If you still feel a little bit timid, you can explore the concept of possibilities in a risk free way by beginning with the gentler question of "What might I be able to do?"

Whether your goal is to restore health, initiate self growth, recovery or transformation, the process always involves sacrifice and a new, broader level of acceptance. Sacrifice might mean letting go of what no longer works for you. It might mean clearing out the clutter in your life and in your self. It might mean making hard choices or taking a stand that reflects integrity. It might involve many different types of simplification. One way or another, you have to get rid of the old, antiquated, outdated, and limiting material that you have accumulated to make room for the new. Since the universe loves gestures that symbolize your life-affirming intentions (such as cleanliness, gentleness, kindness and moderation), try some of these practical ways to demonstrate your commitment to self-improvement, health, and healing.

- Un-clutter your closet.
- Tidy up your workspace.
- Slow your walking pace.
- Reduce your daily chore list.
- Weed the garden.
- Eat more fresh fruits and vegetables.
- Practice loving kindness toward your body and self.
- Practice loving kindness toward others.

Let's get one thing straight. The wounds, traumas, and miseries in your life are not blessings and they are not opportunities. They are hardships. They are hardships that you would never wish on anyone. But they are hardships that you can overcome.
By returning to the reality
of embodiment,
you can recover.
You can be
reborn
as a stronger,
wiser,
compassionate,
more capable,
and
mature
adult.

*Find
pleasure
in
the
simple things..*

*Be
inspired
by the
ordinary..*

# final farewell

mostly it's ok to forget about me
it is right for you to go on living without me.
my time on earth has passed.
it is right for you to continue the story
of your life without me.

every now and then,
just for a moment or two
i hope you think of me
maybe you will sing my favorite song
or eat at my favorite restaurant
and laugh at the memories
of our funniest moments
we had a good time being together.
when you think of those days
be happy, not sad

you are strong
you are capable
it is your duty
to carry on.
now there are others
who depend on you.
yes, you can and yes, you must
move on without me.

for i am not really gone
and though you don't know it
we are as close as ever
i am forever smiling at you
i am forever loving you
and i am with you always.

have a good life, my child
please, carry on.